THE
TEDDY
BEAR
COLLECTION

INTRODUCTION

On cold winter nights, there is nothing bears like better than cuddling up together in front of a glowing fire and telling each other teddy bear tales. Most of all, they like to tell stories about themselves—real bear stories about their lives when non-bears are not there.

Now, for the first time, the Growling (the Chief Council of Bear Affairs) has agreed that some of these stories can be told.

What really happened on the Teddy Bears' Picnic? Where do all the little lost bears go? What happens if a teddy bear meets a *real* bear? Are there bears so tiny you can't see them at all?

Read this collection of exciting, scary, funny, silly stories to learn more about bears than most non-bears ever discover.

Pictures tell stories too from age to age;
Search here and there
For the pawprint of a bear
Hidden on every page.

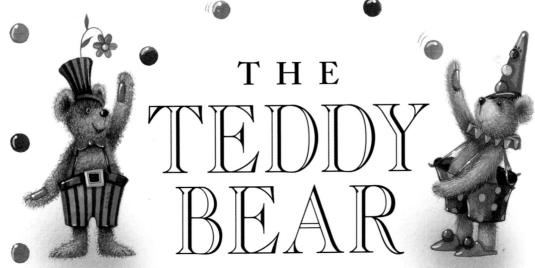

THE
TEDDY
BEAR
COLLECTION

Illustrated by
CATHIE SHUTTLEWORTH

Written by
NICOLA BAXTER

ARMADILLO

FOR TIM ROLFE
C.A.S.

Published by Armadillo Books
an imprint of
Bookmart Limited
Registered Number 2372865
Trading as Bookmart Limited
Desford Road
Enderby
Leicester
LE9 5AD

ISBN 1-90046-518-3

Exclusive to Chapters in Canada

Exclusively distributed in South Africa by CNA Ltd

Produced for Bookmart Limited by Nicola Baxter

Editorial consultant: Ronne Randall
Designer: Amanda Hawkes

Printed in Italy

CONTENTS

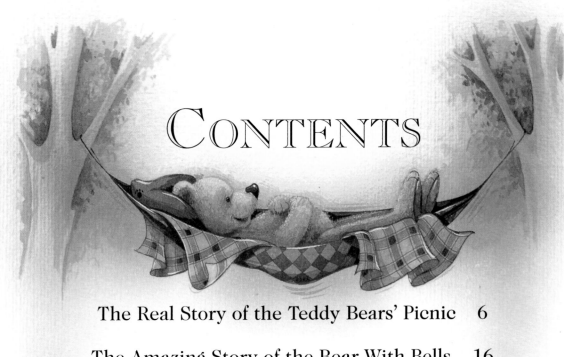

The Real Story of

THE TEDDY BEARS' PICNIC

Colonel Augustus Bearington (retired) here!
Young bears, a lot of stuff and nonsense has
been said about the illustrious event known as
the Teddy Bears' Picnic. Of course, very few of the
fine bears who were present that day still have all
their stitching. I was only a young bear myself, but
I remember it so well. The
time has come to set the
record straight. Throw
another log on the fire,
Mungo. My threadbare
old ears feel the cold.

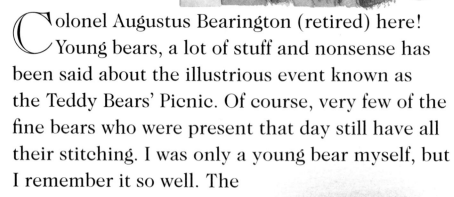

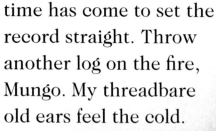

First of all, you must remember that things were different in those days. Today you young bears live in households that may have four or five bears. You have company and can rely on each other in times of trouble. In my young days, bears were less common. Only very lucky children lived with a bear of their own. A bear might stay in the same household for fifty years, passed down from father to son or kept on a shelf in the nursery.

Nurseries! That was another big difference. Children who shared their homes with bears usually spent most of their time in the nursery with a woman called a nanny. She looked after the children while their mother and father were busy, which was all the time except for half an hour in the evening. You may well growl, Mungo. Those nannies did a job that any self-respecting bear could do in his sleep.

Children had to be seen and not heard in those days, and nannies got very cross indeed if they didn't wash behind their ears. Things are very different today. Very different indeed.

In those days, bears were not able to meet very often. The best chance was in the afternoon, when nannies took their charges to the park. Then children would play with friends from other big houses, nannies would chat and knit with other nannies, and bears, of course, could have a word with other bears. It was a part of the day that every bear looked forward to. Luckily, the nanny in the house where I lived liked nothing better than a long chat with her friends. No one paid any attention if a bear strolled off and kept up with his own social life.

I think it was Rufus who first put the idea into our heads. Rufus was a reddish-brown bear from a rather well-to-do home. The little girl he lived with was a Lady. Yes, a real Lady, whose mother was a Duchess. I have moved in very elevated circles in my time, Mungo. I must say that Rufus didn't let his titled family go to his head. He was a friendly, straightforward bear, who never put on airs and graces.

One day, Rufus arrived with interesting news. The Duke and Duchess were giving a party for some Very Important People. There were whispers that the Queen herself would be coming.

"You know, Gussie," said Rufus, "we bears should have a party of our own. We could invite all the Most Important Bears in town and have a day to remember."

Well, the idea caught on at once. Every bear for miles around got wind of the plan somehow, and we soon had a guest list of over a hundred.

"The problem, Rufus old chap," I said one day, "is to find a place big enough for a party of this size. We can't run the risk of being discovered, you know."

Rufus didn't hesitate for a moment.

"We'll hold it right here," he said.

It was obvious! I was a muttonhead not to have thought of it myself. After that, there was no time to lose. I was in charge of arrangements, of course. It takes a military mind to organize an event on that scale. And, modesty aside, I must confess that I also came up with the date for the picnic. Army training came in useful for that, too.

Luckily, several young bears helped with the preparations. You'd be amazed what can be smuggled among a baby's blankets. There were cups, saucers, plates, and food, of course. And some cushions for the old bears. Damp grass is not good for their fur, you know.

At last the great day arrived. It was the day of the Queen's Jubilee. She had been on the throne for umpteen years, and her subjects lined the streets to cheer. Meanwhile, dozens of little bears padded along the back streets, heading for the picnic of a lifetime.

What an afternoon that was! I've never seen so many bears having so much fun.

Ah, and that was the afternoon I met Rosabella. But that's another story.

What was that you said, Mungo? Yes, someone did see us. I don't know who it was. Yes, there was a song. It was quite popular, although the facts were wrong, of course. We were nowhere near the woods. All make believe? Just you look here, young bears. I've carried this worn photograph in my breast pocket for over sixty years.

Ah, yes. It brings a lump to my throat just to look at all those fine faces. Bears were bears in those days. Stir that fire up, Mungo. The smoke's getting in my eyes. Whose turn is it next for a story?

The Amazing Story of
THE BEAR WITH BELLS

Thank you, Colonel. I'm new to your circle, so let me introduce myself. I'm Hermann P. Bear from Switzerland. No, I don't know what the P. stands for, I'm afraid. Now, with all respect, I've found that today's bears are just as brave and clever as the noble bears of yesterday. My story proves just that. And it didn't happen so very long ago, either.

The story concerns a friend of mine, back home among the mountains. I'll call him Fritz. That is not his real name, but he is a modest bear and, if he ever appears in public again, he would not want the world to know the part he played in the Great Zurich Bank Robbery.

Now Fritz is the cleverest, kindest, jolliest bear you could ever hope to meet, but since the day he was sewn, he has suffered a great hardship. Around his neck, his toymaker has put a collar of jingling, jangling, clinking, clanking, ting-a-linging tiny bells.

I can see how horrified you are to hear this. Yes, poor Fritz could not creep off to see his friends during the night. He could not stretch his legs during the day, in case his owner heard him. He was forced to sit quite still, hour after hour, for fear of revealing the great secret of bearness.

Now Fritz was such an unusual bear that he was bought by a collector. Yes, a grown-up person who had over a hundred very beautiful bears. I myself … *ahem* … was one of them. The grown-up was a very rich gentleman, who, in all honesty, cared more about money than bears. He loved us for the francs (that's Swiss money) we were worth, not for the very fine bears we all were.

One day, this gentleman went to America to
buy some more bears. While he was gone, he put
all his dearest possessions in the bank, and that
included some of us bears. It was dreadful. We
were kept in a trunk in a large safe-deposit box,
where a bear had only to move a whisker to set off
dozens of alarms and sirens. I soon learned to
admire Fritz even more. Imagine living like that
all the time!

We had been in the bank for two long weeks, when the Great Robbery took place. Of course, we knew very little about it, inside our trunk. We heard the explosion and felt ourselves being jiggled about as the trunk was carried out, but we only guessed what had happened, as we could see very little through the keyhole of the trunk.

It was some hours later, in a cold Swiss dawn, that the robbers arrived at their hideaway—a cave tucked away in the side of a mountain. They hid their truck among some trees nearby and set about dividing up their ill-gotten gains.

All went well as they opened the boxes containing jewels and gold coins. Then the lid of our trunk was roughly opened and a very unpleasant man peered inside.

I'm afraid that his language, when he saw us sitting there, was quite unrepeatable, especially in front of you younger bears. My ears turned quite pink, I can tell you.

The stupid man had no idea we were valuable bears at all. He kicked the trunk so hard it toppled over, and we fell onto the cold floor of the cave, with icicles dripping down on us. My fur has never been the same since.

It was almost dark when we heard noises outside. It was the police! They had followed the tracks of the robbers' truck to the nearby trees. Now the cave was very well hidden. All the robbers had to do was keep still.

"There was probably a helicopter waiting," I heard a policeman say. "They won't be here now." Now, as you know, humans cannot hear bear speech, so we were powerless to make a noise, but Fritz was a very brave bear indeed. He jumped to his feet and began to jingle and jangle as hard as he could. Every bell around his neck was clinking and clanking. In the silence, it seemed to be an enormous noise.

The most vicious-looking of the robbers—and none of them resembled angels—leaped toward Fritz with a murderous cry. At that moment, a powerful flashlight lit the dramatic scene.

Well, the rest is history. The robbers were
caught, the loot was recovered, and we bears were
taken into custody as evidence. None of the
humans realized whom they had to thank, of
course. But then, we all know that they do not
have our education. Eventually, we were sold to
new owners, all over the world.

And Fritz? Well, I cannot be quite sure. He fell
behind a boulder and was not discovered with the
rest of us. There are sometimes stories of a strange
tinkling, jingling sound to be heard in the
mountains, as though a bear with bells around his
neck might be skidding happily down the slopes.
One or two people have found strange pawprints
in the snow. I hope that Fritz is happy, living the
life of a free and furry bear.

But if you should ever find yourselves in danger in the Alps, dear friends, you might call out the name of Hermann P. Bear. I like to think that a very old friend of mine would come to your aid.

The Sad Story of
THE LITTLE LOST BEARS

The story of Fritz, my friends, has made me think of a subject that is important to all of us. I am speaking, of course, of lost bears. All of us, perhaps, have known bears who have been lost by careless humans. When I was very small, my mother said to me, "Belinda Bear, always stay close to your owner, especially on trains, for there are many little bears today sitting in Lost Property Offices, never to find their way home." I have never forgotten her words.

Well, when I was a little bear, I did not always listen to my mother as well as I should. My friend Bessie and I got into all kinds of trouble. We spent more time in the bathtub than any bear would wish, having jelly, or paint, or honey washed out of our fur. But although we were often in disgrace, we were always careful not to get lost. The idea of the Lost Property Office was *too* horrible. We made sure that the little girl who looked after us *never* left us behind.

One day, Maisie (that was the little girl's name) went to visit her grandmother. And she went by train! Bessie and I were very worried.

"Let's hold paws all the time," said Bessie. "Then, if we get lost, at least we will be together."

So Bessie and I went with Maisie on the train. And I can tell you that trains are *not* safe places for bears. First a large lady put her shopping bag down on top of us and squashed one of my ears. Luckily, Maisie noticed and asked her to move it.

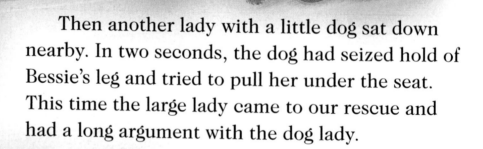

Then another lady with a little dog sat down nearby. In two seconds, the dog had seized hold of Bessie's leg and tried to pull her under the seat. This time the large lady came to our rescue and had a long argument with the dog lady.

Of course, we expect humans to be silly. They don't have a bear's sharp brain, after all. But it was the train itself that caused our biggest problem. With every jiggle and jounce, it jolted us nearer and nearer to the edge of the seat. And let me tell you, those trains jiggle and jounce all the time!

It was sure to happen. As the train rumbled
around a corner, we tumbled onto the floor and
rolled under the table. At that moment, every
single non-bear in the compartment was asleep,
including Maisie and the annoying little dog.

"We'll be left on the train," I moaned. "Then it
will be the Lost Property Office for us."

But Bessie had one of her Good Ideas. Bessie's Good Ideas are sometimes very, very good and sometimes very, very bad. I listened carefully.

"If we climb inside Maisie's overnight bag," she said, "we can't be left behind."

I thought about it. It *did* seem to be a good idea. We climbed into the bag and fell fast asleep. That jiggling, jouncing train has a lot to answer for.

It was dark when we woke up, and we could tell we were no longer on the train.

"We must be in Maisie's grandmother's house," Bessie whispered. Maisie will come soon."

Sure enough, we soon heard footsteps. The bag was opened and a face looked down at us. It was the large lady from the train!

I don't know which of us was more surprised. "Look!" she called to her husband. "These bears belonged to the little girl on the train. What can I do with them?"

It was then that we heard the words we had been dreading.

"Take them to the Lost Property Office," said the man.

"Whatever happens," whispered Bessie, "we mustn't end up you-know-where. We'll escape."

"Is that one of your Good Ideas?" I asked suspiciously.

"No," said Bessie, "it's the only idea there is."

So late that night, when the moon was high in the sky, we crawled out of a downstairs window and set off for home, not knowing which direction to follow or how far away we were.

When morning came, we found we were deep in a forest. Paw in paw, we wandered through the trees, looking for signs that humans were near.

Day after day, we walked on sore paws. We ate berries from the bushes and slept on the soft moss among the roots of the trees. Once a bad bird tried to peck out our fur to line its nest, but Bessie was good at growling and frightened it away. Once I fell into a hole in a tree and only just managed to climb out again.

At night, we often cried ourselves to sleep.

One afternoon, we were found by a family
taking a walk. The little girl brought me here to
join you all and gave Bessie to her cousin. From
that day to this, I have never seen Bessie or
Maisie, and my furry face is often wet with tears.
If there were human children listening to me now,
I would tell them to cuddle their bears and keep
them safe, for in my dreams, I often see Maisie's
little face and hope that she has found a new bear
to make her happy.

The Scary Story of

THE GHOSTLY BEAR

Little bears, the story I am about to tell is very, very scary. If you get frightened, you must put your paws over your ears and cuddle up to a grown-up bear.

When I was a very little bear myself, my aunty told me this tale. She was a very sensible bear, so I am sure that every word is true.

Once upon a time, in a faraway land, there was
a huge castle. It was tall and dark. Vines covered
the turrets and many of the dusty windows. Bats
fluttered from the battlements.

The castle stood empty for many years, but
one day there was great excitement in the nearby
village. It was said that the owner of the castle was
coming to visit. Now no one had ever seen this
mysterious owner, so there was a great deal of talk
about who it might be.

"I've heard it is a
Countess," said the
baker. "She was once
very beautiful. Then a
witch put a curse on
her. Since then she has
always worn a veil to
hide her ugly face."

"No, no," replied
the blacksmith, "the
owner *is* a witch. She
travels at night, and has
a black cat."

"Nonsense!" The
schoolteacher waved
her stick. "It is simply
an old lady who cannot
move around very well.
That is why she has not
visited for a long time."

Every day, the children in the village looked out for the important visitor, but no one came along the winding road from the forest. Then, one morning, a little girl called Lucy noticed smoke rising above the highest tower in the castle.

"She must have come in the night!" she called to everyone she met. "She is a witch after all."

When they heard this, the villagers were very worried. "We must take her a big present," they said, "so she does not get angry with us. Who knows what spells she might cast if she feels we are unfriendly."

That seemed to be a good idea, so a collection was made and a beautiful chest was bought to be given to the witch (if that was what she was).

"Now," said the baker, "who will give the present to the witch? I cannot go with my weak heart and that long, winding path to climb."

"Nor can I," said the teacher, "with my bad leg."

For one reason or another, not one of the grown-ups in the village could deliver the present to the mysterious visitor.

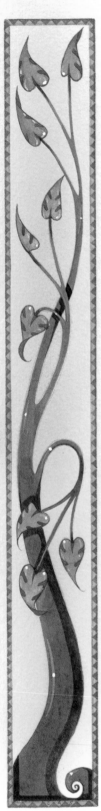

"I'll go," said Lucy. "I'd like to see what she looks like."

"But," said the blacksmith, "won't you be frightened?"

"Oh no," replied Lucy. "I will take my teddy bear with me. He'll keep me safe."

She certainly was a very sensible little girl.

That afternoon, Lucy set off to the castle, carrying her bear and the chest. It was a long climb up the winding path, but at last she stood before the doors of the castle and knocked.

As she stood there, all by herself, Lucy began to feel just a little bit frightened. But she clutched her old bear and started to sing to keep her spirits up. For a long time, nothing happened. Then, with a horrible creaking noise, the doors of the castle slowly opened—all by themselves.

There really was not much to do but walk straight in, and Lucy was beginning to feel that anything was better than standing on the doorstep.

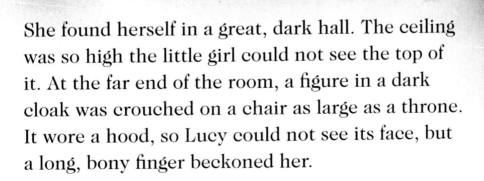

She found herself in a great, dark hall. The ceiling was so high the little girl could not see the top of it. At the far end of the room, a figure in a dark cloak was crouched on a chair as large as a throne. It wore a hood, so Lucy could not see its face, but a long, bony finger beckoned her.

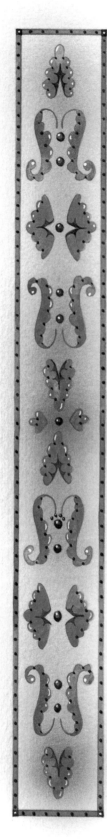

When the little girl was standing in front of the figure at last, she tried to speak up bravely, though there was a quiver in her voice.

"Please, your highness, or your witchness, we all wanted to welcome you to the castle and give you this present."

A horrible cackle came from the dark-robed figure. "A chest? I've got hundreds of them," it croaked. "But I can see that you do have something I want. Give me that teddy bear, and I will let you go home safely."

"No!" cried Lucy, hugging her teddy bear. "You can't have him."

"Really?" replied the voice. "Then I shall have to lock you up until you agree."

The next thing Lucy knew, she was being dragged into a room containing an enormous four-poster bed, and the door of the room was being locked behind her.

Lucy stayed in that room until it began to get dark. Then the dark figure brought her some food and a single candle.

"Go to bed," it said. "Let's see if you feel so brave in the morning."

Lucy climbed into bed and pulled the covers
up to her chin. She felt more frightened than she
ever had in her life, but somehow, she managed to
go to sleep.

At midnight, she was woken by a clock clanging loudly near her bed.

Dong! Dong! Dong!

She woke to find a large, white bear standing by her bed. He seemed to be shimmering with a strange light.

"W...w...what do you want?" she asked.

The strange bear said nothing, but it held out its furry paws toward Lucy's little bear, tucked up beside her in the bed.

"No!" cried Lucy. "He's mine!"

But then she saw an extraordinary thing. Large crystal tears were running down the shining bear's face and dripping onto the little girl's bed.

He looked so very sad that Lucy could not bear it. "All right," she said quietly. "Don't be sad. Here's my own special bear to cheer you up." And she handed her own teddy bear to the strange, ghostly visitor.

With a sigh, holding the little bear gently in his arms, the shining bear turned away. Lucy watched as he walked toward the door … and melted straight through it! Lucy shut her eyes and rubbed them. When she opened them, she was back in her own room at home, tucked up in her own little bed. Only her teddy bear was missing.

Next morning, the whole village gathered in
amazement at the foot of the hill. Overnight, the
castle had changed in an extraordinary way. The
windows were sparkling. The vine had been cut.
There were flags flying from the turrets and white
doves fluttering around the battlements.

"It must have been
bewitched after all,"
gasped the villagers.
"Our act of kindness in
sending the chest has
broken the spell. That
is often the way in
old stories."

Lucy thought about what had happened. She
thought about the chest hidden under her bed.

"Someone was unhappy," she thought. "And
now they are not. That is what bears are for."

I believe she was right, my friends. The mystery never was solved. Later it was said that the Countess who lived in the castle had suffered an unhappy childhood. Perhaps returning to the castle of her birth had brought a smile to her face again. Only Lucy had a different idea.

The Funny Story of
The Bear Who Was Bare

My dears, after that rather scary tale, I have one that is not in the least bit frightening. You can come out from behind that chair, young bears. Uncle Bill Bear has a much sillier tale to tell you. This story is about a bare bear. A bare bear? I mean, of course, a bear wearing nothing at all— not even his fur! Let me tell you how it happened.

Once there was a bear called Edwin Dalrymple Devereux Yeldon III. He said that his friends called him Eddy, but as a matter of fact, this bear did not have many friends at all. And that was because he was simply not a very nice bear. Oh, he was very handsome, with long, golden fur that shone in the sunlight, but that was where the problem began. Eddy thought he was better than other bears, with his long name and fancy fur.

"Pass me my fur brush," he would say. "The breeze has ruffled me terribly. You other bears need not worry, of course, with your short, rough, ordinary fur."

When the bears played leap-bear or hide-and-seek in the nursery, Eddy always refused to play. "Those are very rough games," he complained. "I might get my paws dirty. Games are too silly for superior bears like myself."

Well, after a while, all the other bears were sick of Edwin and his airs and graces. I'm afraid that some young bears tried to think of ways of teaching Eddy a lesson. But as things turned out, they did not need to. Edwin Dalrymple Devereux Yeldon III brought about his own downfall.

One day, Eddy was boasting about all the famous bears he knew. One or two of the other bears wondered out loud if his tales were really true, which made Eddy furious. "You'll see," he said. "I'll write a letter to my friend Prince Bearovski. He's sure to write back at once, and then you'll see."

But as Eddy carried a huge bottle of ink across the room, his furry feet tripped on the edge of the rug. Down fell teddy Eddy. Up flew the bottle of ink. *Splat!* The bottle hit the floor, and ink flew everywhere! There was ink on Eddy's nose and ink on his ears. His paws and his knees had bright blue splashes too. For a second, there was silence. Then Eddy let out a horrible roar. "You stupid bears!" he cried. "Just look at my fur! Who put that rug in the way?" And that was really not very fair, for the rug had been there for years and years.

Teddy Eddy sulked for the rest of the day. But worse was to follow. Next morning, the little girl who lived there saw what had happened to her most beautiful bear. Without asking anyone else at all, she decided that Eddy needed a bath.

The other bears peeked around the bathroom door to watch the proceedings. There were bubbles everywhere! Only the tip of teddy Eddy's nose could be seen. Giggling and chuckling, the bears went back to the nursery and waited for Eddy to reappear.

They waited all that day and all that night. But Eddy did not return. Next day, there was no sign of him.

"That little girl is not very sensible," said one bear. "She may have left him in the water. We really should go and see if he's all right, my friends."

But teddy Eddy was not in the bathtub. The bears were just about to go away again, when one little bear noticed that one of the cupboards was not quite closed.

Inside sat Edwin Dalrymple Devereux Yeldon III, wrapped from ears to paws in a large towel.

"Come on, Eddy," called the young bear mischievously, "you must be dry by now."

"No," said Eddy. "I ... er ... I can't."

"But it must be very boring in this cupboard," said another bear.

"No," said Eddy. "It's ... er ... very pleasant. Please go away."

"Oh come on," laughed two of the smallest bears. And they tugged playfully at the towel. Eddy tried hard to hold onto it, but it was no use. As the towel slipped away, every bear could see ... Edwin Dalrymple Devereux Yeldon III was bare! When the little girl washed away the ink, Eddy's fur was washed away too.

Poor Eddy. He couldn't hide any more. Slowly, he walked back to the nursery and sat down in the darkest corner. The old, proud Edwin Dalrymple Devereux Yeldon III was gone. A very different bear remained.

For a few days, the other bears smiled to themselves about what had happened. But after a while, they began to feel rather sorry for Eddy.

"I think we should help him," said one old bear. "Apart from anything else, he must be cold without his fur."

"That's true," said another bear. "Why don't we make him some clothes?"

Over the next few days, the bears had great fun. They used up all the old scraps of material that they could find and made some very grand clothes. There was a hat with a feather, a cloak with tassels, some striped trousers, and some shiny black boots.

When he saw them, Eddy was overwhelmed by the bears' kindness.

"Thank you, my friends," he said, as he put on the clothes. "I know that I have not been a very nice bear in the past, but I will try to do better now. In following all that is good and kind and bearlike, I will be absolutely fearless. Or perhaps I should say, in spite of my fine clothes, my dears, absolutely furless!"

The Short Story of

THE LITTLEST BEAR

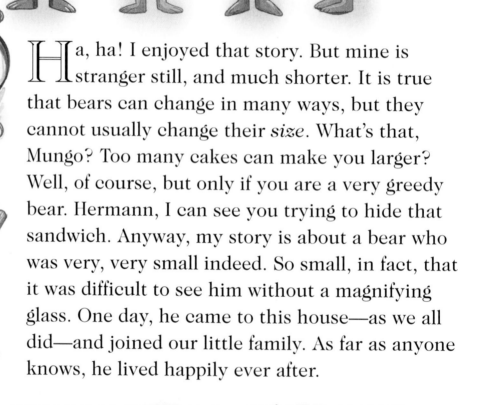

Ha, ha! I enjoyed that story. But mine is stranger still, and much shorter. It is true that bears can change in many ways, but they cannot usually change their *size*. What's that, Mungo? Too many cakes can make you larger? Well, of course, but only if you are a very greedy bear. Hermann, I can see you trying to hide that sandwich. Anyway, my story is about a bear who was very, very small indeed. So small, in fact, that it was difficult to see him without a magnifying glass. One day, he came to this house—as we all did—and joined our little family. As far as anyone knows, he lived happily ever after.

What? No, there isn't any more to the story. I told you it was short. The bear was so small that he disappeared on the day he came here and has never been seen since. I imagine he is here with us now, but it would take a bear with sharper eyes than mine to see him. Why don't you all take a look around?

The Unusual Story of

The Real Teddy Bear

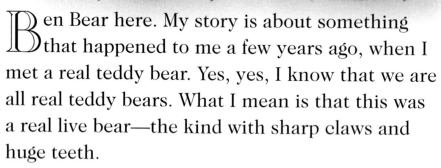

Ben Bear here. My story is about something that happened to me a few years ago, when I met a real teddy bear. Yes, yes, I know that we are all real teddy bears. What I mean is that this was a real live bear—the kind with sharp claws and huge teeth.

Here is what happened. My owner at the time was a little boy who was very fond of food. Wherever we went, he always made sure that he had a bag of goodies with him. "Just in case," he said, "we get caught in an avalanche, or stranded in the desert, or trapped by a flood." Not one of those things was at all likely to happen, but Joseph (that was his name) felt happier if he had some provisions with him.

You can imagine that this was particularly true when he went camping with his friends. All the boys brought food to cook on the campfire, but Joseph brought extra supplies, just in case.

One year, we went deep into the woods. The boys put up their tents and went off to explore. Joseph left me in his tent. Now that I am an older and wiser bear, I realize that he did not want his friends to see me, in case they thought he was a baby. But Joseph looked at me very seriously and said, "Now Ben, your job is to stay here and guard the food!" And I was a young bear who took his job seriously in those days.

The boys were gone for a long time. At first I could hear their shouts echoing through the trees, but soon there was silence. Only the wind could be heard, rustling the branches.

I believe I dozed off for a while, because the next thing I knew, I was wide awake and listening to a very different sound. It was a snorting, sniffling, crunching, munching sort of a noise. I wasn't frightened, of course, but I did wish I knew just what was stomping and chomping outside the tent.

The sounds got louder and louder. Then I heard the sound of the tent flap being unzipped. *Zoooooooooooooooop!*

A brown furry face peered in. It was a bear! A real bear!

For a long, long moment, I looked at the bear.
And the bear looked at me. Then, all of a sudden,
he opened his mouth and said, "Hello! Anything
to eat in here?"

Well, you could have knocked me down
with a feather. He was speaking bear
language, of course, but I found it was
not very different from the way we
teddy bears speak, so I could
understand him fairly well. He
seemed friendly, and I was just
thinking how nice it would be
to get to know him, when I
remembered what Joseph
had said to me.

"No," I said firmly.
"No food in here at all."

But the bear was already sniffing the air and looking suspiciously at the large bag beside me. "Really?" he said. "That's very strange. I'm pretty sure I can smell sausages and beans and chocolate cake."

I thought quickly. "That's very clever of you," I said. "There *were* sausages and beans and chocolate cake, but the boys have eaten them all."

"Any leftovers?" asked the bear. "Any crumbs at all?"

"None at all," I replied, shaking my head sadly.

"More supplies coming?" asked the bear eagerly. "Tomorrow, perhaps?"

"I don't think so," I answered. "We're going home in the morning."

The bear nodded his head. "Ho hum," he said. "It's my birthday, you know. I just thought I might find a birthday treat around her somewhere. Well, nice meeting you." And as he ambled away into the forest, I was quite sure I could hear his furry tummy rumbling.

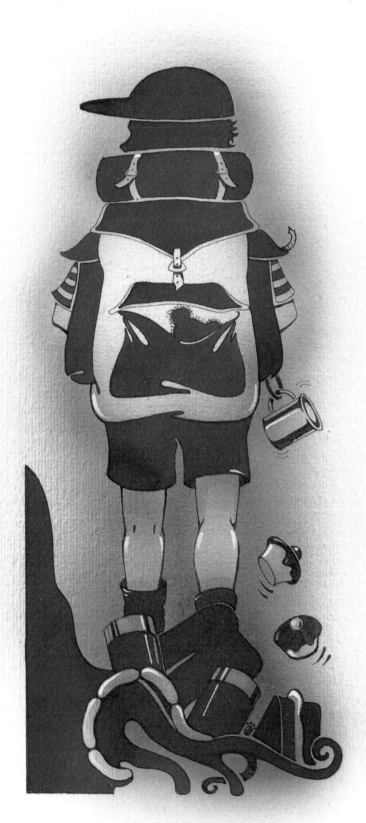

A little while later, the boys came back and made their supper. I kept a wary eye on the shadows between the trees, expecting to see some large furry ears or a sniffly snout. But there was no sign of the bear at all.

Next morning, as planned, we packed up our things and set off for home.

"Now, have we got everything?" asked Joseph. "Let's go!"

By this stage, of course, I was well hidden in Joseph's backpack, so that the other boys would not see me. Otherwise I might have mentioned to him that the special emergency supplies bag had fallen behind the stump of a tree, helped along just a bit by a nudge from my elbow.

Joseph was a little upset when he found that his goodies were gone. But it was far too late to go back into the dark forest to find them, and after all, there were plenty more at home.

As I sat on Joseph's pillow that night, I looked up at the big yellow moon peeking in at the window and imagined the friendly bear, sitting down in the moonlight to enjoy a special snack.

"Happy birthday, bear," I whispered. "Happy birthday!"

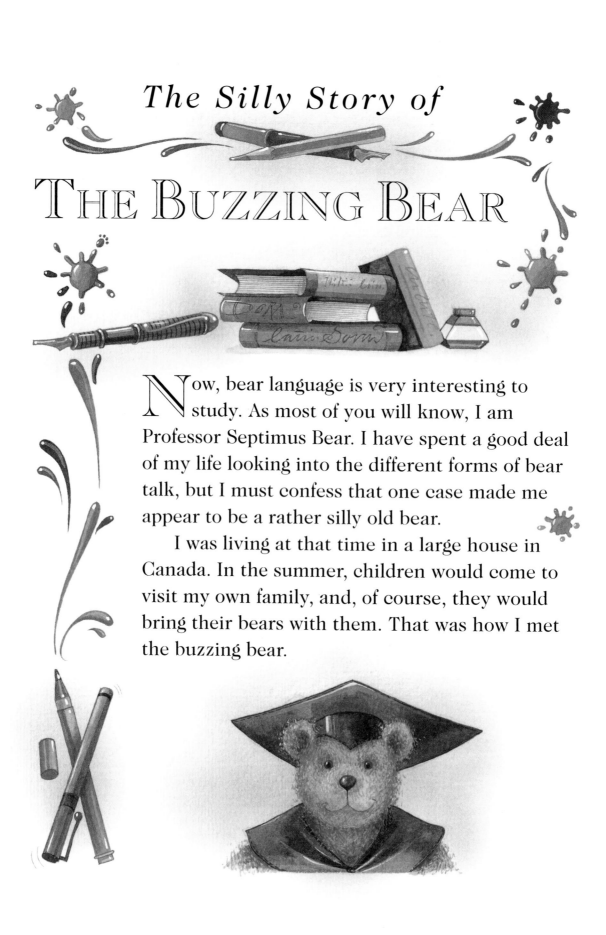

The Silly Story of
THE BUZZING BEAR

Now, bear language is very interesting to study. As most of you will know, I am Professor Septimus Bear. I have spent a good deal of my life looking into the different forms of bear talk, but I must confess that one case made me appear to be a rather silly old bear.

I was living at that time in a large house in Canada. In the summer, children would come to visit my own family, and, of course, they would bring their bears with them. That was how I met the buzzing bear.

This bear came to the house on a fine, sunny day. He was a large, fluffy bear, with golden yellow fur. Of course, I tried to make him welcome.

"Good morning," I said. "My name is Septimus. Will you tell me yours?"

"Buzz!" said the bear.

"Er … Buzz? Well, it's very nice to meet you, Mr. Buzz. Have you had a long journey?"

"Buzz!" said the bear.

"I'm sorry? Did you say that you have come from far away?"

"Buzz! Buzz! Buzz!" said the strange bear.

Well, I must admit, I was puzzled. I went straight to my reference books to find out if there was a distant country where bears only buzzed. I read and read until darkness fell.

But all my research was in vain. I read about the hooting bears of Borneo and the singing bears of Thailand. I found an article about an African bear language that has all kinds of sounds in it and is impossible for other bears to pronounce. But I could find nothing at all about buzzing bears.

At first I was disappointed. Then I realized the great opportunity that had been presented to me. I could be the very first bear to study this extraordinary language. I saw myself giving lectures to other clever bears around the world. I imagined signing copies of my famous book on the subject. A rosy future was surely before me.

At once, I picked up a new notebook and pencil and set off to find the bear.

The buzzing bear was sitting rather sadly in a chair. I sat down beside him and began to take notes as I asked him questions.

"Are you a bear?" I asked.

"Buzz!" he said.

Aha, I thought, one buzz means yes.

"Are you an elephant?" I asked.

"Buzz! BUZZ!" said the bear.

I decided that two buzzes must mean no.

"Are you a giraffe?" I enquired.

"Buzz!"

My friends, I admit, I was very confused. Then I suddenly realized that the bear might not be able to understand me at all! But how was I to learn buzz language in order to speak to him? I did not know how to say the simplest thing.

It was a beautiful day, so I took the bear by the arm and led him gently out into the garden. By the house was an enormous cedar tree. I led the bear up to it and patted its trunk firmly.

"Tree," I said. "Tree."

"Buzz!" said the bear.

I walked over to a shady seat.

"Chair," I repeated, pointing. "Chair. Chair."

You can probably guess what the bear said.

After half an hour, I was at my wit's end. We had made no progress at all, and I was afraid that my reputation as a scholar was at stake. Would anyone ever take my work seriously again, I wondered?

At last, tired and depressed, I invited the bear to sit down by a beautiful flower border.

We had only been sitting for a moment when, "Buzz! BUZZ! BUZZZZZZZZ!" The loudest buzzing I had ever heard filled my ears. And out of the strange *bear's* ears flew first one and then another big, yellow, buzzing bee!

"What a relief!" said the bear. "I haven't been able to hear a thing with those bees buzzing in there!"

Well, we both rolled on the grass laughing, and I have tried hard not to be such a pompous old bear ever since!

The Strange Story of
THE ADVENTUROUS BEAR

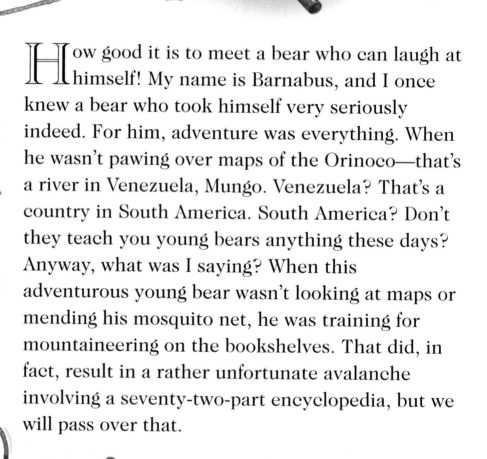

How good it is to meet a bear who can laugh at himself! My name is Barnabus, and I once knew a bear who took himself very seriously indeed. For him, adventure was everything. When he wasn't pawing over maps of the Orinoco—that's a river in Venezuela, Mungo. Venezuela? That's a country in South America. South America? Don't they teach you young bears anything these days? Anyway, what was I saying? When this adventurous young bear wasn't looking at maps or mending his mosquito net, he was training for mountaineering on the bookshelves. That did, in fact, result in a rather unfortunate avalanche involving a seventy-two-part encyclopedia, but we will pass over that.

Now, strangely enough, it was that very accident that led to the story I am about to tell you. For one of the volumes of the encyclopedia fell open at a page about a man who went around the world in eighty days. No sooner had he read this, than our friend—let's call him B.—was determined he would be the very first bear to travel right around the world.

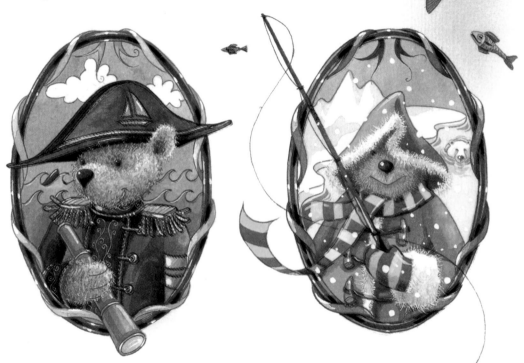

"You will need to beware of sharks," said an old seafaring bear. "Their teeth are sharper than any bear's."

"You will have to look out for icebergs," said another bear. "And the white bears who live on them are very fierce."

"Don't forget to send us some postcards," said a little bear, who was making a collection.

B. spent months preparing for his trip. By the time he was ready, he was so loaded down with equipment, he could hardly walk.

"Good luck!" called all the bears together, as he staggered off down the path.

Well, eighty days passed. And then another eighty. There was no news from the adventurer.

"It's not surprising," said one old bear. "There are no mailboxes at all in the middle of the desert, you know."

Then, one morning, a postcard arrived. It showed a picture of the Eiffel Tower. On the back, there were just three words: *Reached France. B.*

The following month, another postcard was delivered. It showed the Leaning Tower of Pisa. The message said: *Crossing Italy. B.*

No one was very surprised when a third card arrived a few weeks later. It showed the Great Wall of China. The adventurer had written: *Learning Chinese. B.*

Next month, the excited bears waited for a postcard to drop onto the doormat. At last it came, showing a Spanish flamenco dancer. The message read: *In Spain. B.*

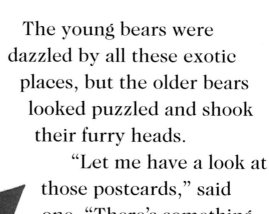

The young bears were dazzled by all these exotic places, but the older bears looked puzzled and shook their furry heads.

"Let me have a look at those postcards," said one. "There's something odd about our friend's route, you know."

Sure enough, when they looked closely at the postcards, everyone could see that all of them had been sent from Mountville, just a few miles away.

"I think some of us need to go on an expedition too," said the older bears.

Once again, a bear expedition was waved off from the front door, but this time, they returned before nightfall, bringing with them a very crestfallen young bear.

"I did try," he said, "but all my baggage was *so* heavy, and the world is *so* big that I came home again—only I couldn't face you all."

The oldest bear put a fatherly arm around my shoulders. "We are just happy to have you home," he said. "Come in and tell us all about your adventures."

Oh, I see that I have given the secret away. Yes, my friends, I was that foolish young bear. And I can tell you it is much better to be sitting here with you than in Turkey or Tasmania or Thailand or Timbuktu.

The Christmas Story of
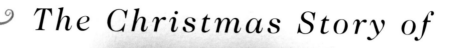

BEARS EVERYWHERE

ungo here! My story reminds us of a time of the year that is very special for bears. Yes, I mean Christmas. Many bears move to new homes then, as they are given as presents to new little girls or boys. But we bears know that we have a special job to do at Christmas time, and it is one that human beings do not know about at all. So cuddle a little closer, dear friends, in case one of those curious little people is listening.

Now, you know as well as I do that humans make a lot of mistakes. I mean the kind of mistakes that sensible bears would never make— losing their socks, tripping over their shoelaces, and forgetting each other's birthday, for example. At Christmas time they are worse than ever. Sooner or later, some silly human is likely to send the wrong present to the wrong person.

We bears, who understand how important it is to feel loved and wanted, know that someone who receives the wrong present will feel upset. Perhaps even cross. So that is why our special job at Christmas is to look out for misplaced presents and send them back to where they belong. The Teddy Bear International Mail Service was set up especially for that purpose.

One Christmas, a forgetful granny in England made a particularly bad mistake. She sent woolly gloves to her niece in Australia, where it is hot at Christmas time, and a sunhat to her niece in Canada, where the snow lay thick on the ground. And to make matters worse, she sent them at the very last minute, so it was not until the last delivery on Christmas Eve that the wrong presents arrived at the right addresses. Or the right presents arrived at the wrong addresses. You know what I mean.

★ What could the T.B.I.M.S. do with so little time to spare? Even if two intrepid bears were to squeeze onto last-minute flights from airports in both countries, they would not arrive in time. A council meeting of the Growling was called at once, and the Oldest Bear of All was consulted.

"Dear bears," he said, in his quavering voice, "you have done well to bring this distressing matter to my attention. I can see only one solution, and it is one that we can use only in the most serious cases. These presents will have to be … *ahem* … lost … until Christmas is over. Please alert the bears concerned at once."

Just as soon as messages could reach the bears at opposite sides of the world, action was taken.

The parcel containing the gloves was dropped carefully behind the cushions of a couch. The package containing the sunhat, which was much bigger, was tucked into the top of a cupboard full of odds and ends. (The kind of untidy human cupboard that decent bears simply cannot bear!)

Now normally in this kind of situation, action is taken immediately after Christmas. The presents are exchanged and then allowed to be discovered, usually with whoops of delight, in those rather dark days after the festive season. But for some reason, both sets of bears in this case forgot all about the "missing" presents.

Yes, yes, I know. It is unpardonable. It is, as you say, Hubert, as bad as the humans themselves. Yes, I would put it that strongly. In fact, it was not until six months later that teddy bears playing on the couch in Australia discovered the offending package. In horror, they at once contacted their Canadian cousins, and that parcel was retrieved as well. Now both sets of bears were at a loss to know what to do.

The bears reported to the next meeting of the Growling as they should. There were gasps of horror around the room. Then, in the silence that followed, the Oldest Bear of All told those bears exactly what he thought of them. And it wasn't very complimentary, I can tell you.

"Sir," said one of the bears concerned, "we are more sorry than we can say. We will make the exchange at once."

But at this the Oldest Bear smiled. "I think you will find," he said, "that no exchange will now be necessary. Simply allow the presents to be found. But make sure that this NEVER happens again."

The bears were puzzled, but they did as they were told. The niece in Australia was delighted with her gloves. The niece in Canada just loved her sunhat. And both of them were pleased and puzzled to find a Christmas present so long after Christmas. Well, that puzzle is no mystery to us, my friends. But which of you clever bears can tell me why the presents did not need to be changed?

The Secret Story of
THE BEARS WHO WERE BRAVE

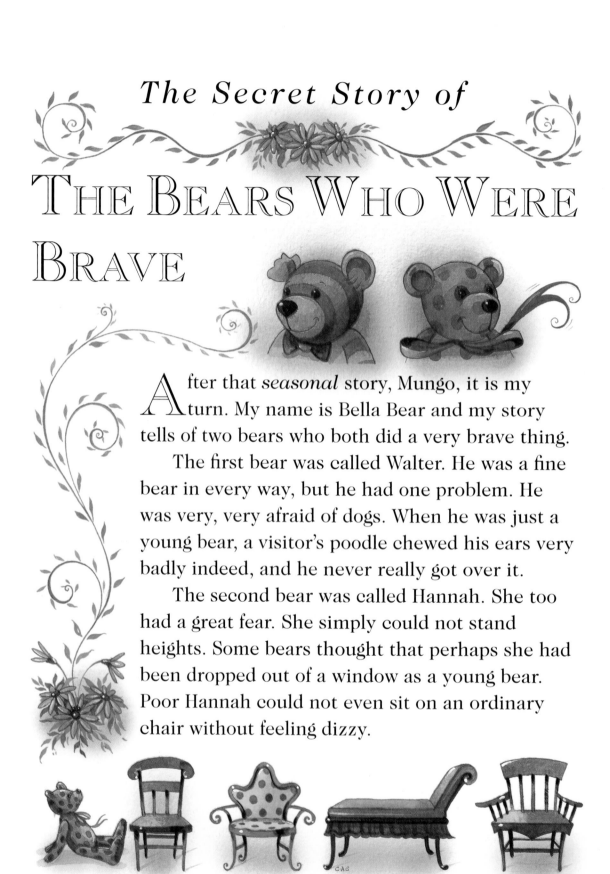

After that *seasonal* story, Mungo, it is my turn. My name is Bella Bear and my story tells of two bears who both did a very brave thing.

The first bear was called Walter. He was a fine bear in every way, but he had one problem. He was very, very afraid of dogs. When he was just a young bear, a visitor's poodle chewed his ears very badly indeed, and he never really got over it.

The second bear was called Hannah. She too had a great fear. She simply could not stand heights. Some bears thought that perhaps she had been dropped out of a window as a young bear. Poor Hannah could not even sit on an ordinary chair without feeling dizzy.

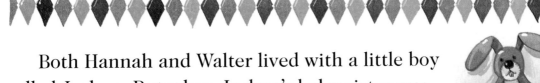

Both Hannah and Walter lived with a little boy called Joshua. But when Joshua's baby sister was born, Joshua said he was too old for teddy bears, and he gave Hannah and Walter to the baby. Yes, you may laugh, my friends. We know that no human is ever too old for a teddy bear.

◆ Anyway, Joshua was a little bit upset by the amount of attention that the baby received, so his parents gave him a baby of his own—a little puppy called Jack. Jack went everywhere with Joshua, and he really was rather like a baby. He whimpered when he was hungry, and he made little puddles on the cushions, which Joshua tried to hide from the grown-ups.

One day, Hannah and Walter were left in the garden when the children were taken inside for their lunch.

Suddenly, the bears heard a frightened little bark. Somehow, the naughty puppy had managed to climb onto the roof of the summerhouse. He was stuck.

"We must rescue that puppy," said Hannah.

"Why?" asked Walter.

"Because if we don't, he'll jump and hurt himself," explained his friend. "And he is a very sweet puppy."

"Hmph," said Walter.

"And Joshua loves him," Hannah added.

"All right," said Walter, "but *you* can do it, because I'm not going anywhere near him. Oh no."

"But I can't go up there!" cried Hannah. "It's much too high!"

The two little bears sat miserably looking at the puppy. Then both of them spoke at once.

"I'll go if you will," they said.

So Hannah and Walter helped each other up onto the summerhouse roof (and Hannah only had her eyes shut half the time). Then they showed the silly puppy how to get down (and Walter only hid behind Hannah because there wasn't much room to stand).

And from that day to this, none of the humans in the house know how brave the little bears were. But the puppy knew, and I think he told Joshua, because a few days later, the little boy decided that his sister was too *small* for teddy bears, and he tucked Hannah and Walter into *his* bed again. Which is how it should be, after all.

The Sleepy Story of
THE BEAR WHO COULDN'T STAY AWAKE

My friends, the fire is burning low and the smallest bears have fallen asleep on our laps. Perhaps we should all go off to bed now. What? One more story? Well, if you are sure.

My story is of a very sleepy bear called Selina. Whenever she was wanted, Selina was always to be found dozing in a corner. Some bears were rather suspicious about Selina's sleeping. Somehow, when there was a treat in store, such as extra honey or a birthday party, Selina was always awake. When there was tidying to be done, or muddy pawprints to be removed, or honeypots to wash, Selina would be snoring quietly somewhere.

"If you ask me," grumbled the Oldest Bear of All, "that lazy little bear is just pretending. She needs to be taught a lesson."

"Bears do need their sleep," explained her friend Marilyn anxiously. "Selina would be so upset if she knew what horrible things were being said about her. And she has slept right through suppertime. She wouldn't do that if she was really awake. She's always very hungry."

At that moment, Selina gave an extra loud snore.

The older bears shook their heads. "If she is pretending," they said, "she will wake up after we are asleep and have a little snack then. What we must do is stay awake tonight and watch carefully to see what happens."

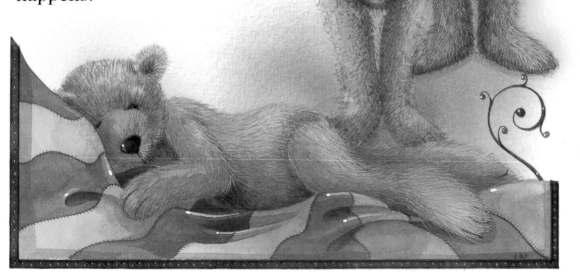

So five bears volunteered not to go to bed. As it grew dark, they took up their positions and watched the sleeping Selina.

Very soon, the first little bear's nose began to twitch. He was trying to stop himself from yawning. Then his bright little eyes began to close. In just two minutes, he was fast asleep.

The second little bear struggled hard to stay awake. He patted his head with his paws to stop himself from drifting off to sleep. But his patting grew slower, and slower, and slower … until he too was dreaming a teddy-bear dream.

The third bear was older than the first two. He was quite determined to stay awake. He decided to march up and down—quietly, of course. *Pad, pad, pad,* he marched across the floor. *Pad, pad, pad,* back he came. *Pad, pad, pad … pad, pad, pad.* He looked as if he was awake. He sounded as if he was awake. But before long, that bear was sleep-walking! His eyes were closed, but his little legs were still moving. In his furry head, he dreamed of being a soldier on parade.

✱ The fourth and fifth watching bears decided to keep each other awake. They talked in whispers late into the night. But there is something very soft and sleepy about whispering. Although they tried hard to stay awake, soon the whispers became gentle snores.

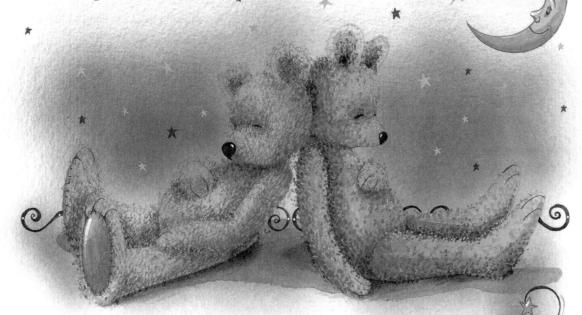

In the morning, the other bears crowded round to see what had happened.

"Well … *ahem*," said the first bear, "I certainly didn't see her wake up." ★

"Er … neither did I," agreed the second bear.

"I was on duty all night," said the third bear, "and I didn't hear a sound."

The fourth and fifth bears looked at each other, and scratched their furry heads. "I saw nothing unusual," said one, truthfully. "Did you, old pal?"

"Nothing at all," replied his friend firmly.

So the mystery of the sleeping bear never was solved. But Selina, who was sleeping happily in her usual place, gave an extra loud snore and the tiniest, sleepy, secret smile.

Now it is time for little bears everywhere to go to sleep. Goodnight, little bears! Goodnight!